THE SAGA OF DARREN SHAN
THE VAMPIRE'S ASSISTANT

VOLUME
2

Story: Darren Shan
Manga: Takahiro Arai

DARREN SHAN LEADS THE LIFE OF A HEALTHY, HAPPY YOUNG BOY...BUT HIS FATE TAKES A TURN FOR THE WORSE ON THE NIGHT HE GOES TO SEE THE CIRQUE DU FREAK WITH HIS BEST FRIEND, STEVE. WHEN THE CIRQUE'S POISONOUS SPIDER BITES STEVE ON THE NECK, DARREN MUST ASK THE SPIDER'S OWNER, THE VAMPIRE LARTEN CREPSLEY, FOR HELP. MR. CREPSLEY IS ABLE TO FULFILL DARREN'S REQUEST, BUT THERE IS A FEE TO BE PAID: DARREN MUST BECOME A VAMPIRE! HIS PEACEFUL LIFE GONE, DARREN MUST NOW VENTURE INTO THE NIGHT ON A JOURNEY WITH HIS NEW VAMPIRE MASTER....

THE VAMPIRE'S ASSISTANT
CONTENTS

AH, WHAT A LOVELY NIGHT...

OH, WE ARE THE NEWCASTLE TROOP 15~!

♪

HI-HO, HI-HO!

♪

CAN I HELP YOU, SON? ARE YOU LOST?

CHAPTER 5: THE LIFE OF A VAMPIRE

COME ON, LET'S —

HARA (TRIK)

POOR LITTLE FELLA. DON'T WORRY, I'M A SCOUT MASTER WITH THE BOY SCOUTS.

FURU

FURU (SHAKE)

CHAPTER 5:
THE LIFE OF A VAMPIRE

THEY DID NOT HAVE THEM IN MY DAY.

WERE YOU EVER IN THE SCOUTS?

I THOUGHT HE WAS YOUNGER.

IMAGINE A MAN HIS AGE WEARING SHORTS ...

MOZO

MOZO (RUSTLE)

IT'S A SPECIAL GAS I BREATHED INTO HIM TO MAKE HIM SLEEP, THAT IS ALL.

DO NOT MAKE ME REPEAT MYSELF, DARREN.

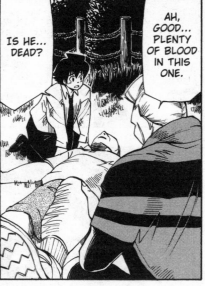

IS HE... DEAD?

AH, GOOD... PLENTY OF BLOOD IN THIS ONE.

SU (ZSH)

YOU CANNOT DO THAT, THOUGH.

YOU ARE NOT A FULL VAMPIRE YET.

YOUR TURN, DARREN.

UGH...

GOKU

GOKU (GLUG)

THAT'S DIFFERENT. THIS IS A HUMAN!

DO NOT BE STUPID. IT IS TIME YOU DRANK!

YOU HAVE DRUNK ANIMAL BLOOD!

NO! I CAN'T!

WE ARE ONLY TAKING A SMALL AMOUNT OF BLOOD.

YOU MUST UNDERSTAND, DARREN, THAT WE ARE NOT HARMING OR KILLING HUMANS.

I KNOW, YOU'VE EXPLAINED IT TO ME!

IF YOU DO NOT START DRINKING HUMAN BLOOD, YOU WILL GROW WEAK AND EVENTUALLY DIE.

EVEN HALF-VAMPIRES CANNOT LIVE ON ANIMAL BLOOD ALONE.

KUCHU (LICK)

FUU (SIGH)...

BUT I JUST CAN'T...

I CAN'T DRINK HUMAN BLOOD ...

VERY WELL. I WILL LET YOU ABSTAIN THIS TIME.

TSULUU (SMEAR)

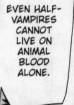

WHAT SORT OF CLOTHING IS THE STYLE OF THESE TIMES?

DAR-REN?

I MIGHT BE HALF-VAMPIRE...

THIS CIRCUS OUTFIT IS TOO NOTICE-ABLE.

WE ARE CLOSE TO TOWN. BETTER FIND NEW CLOTHES.

BUT IT IS AN ISSUE YOU MUST FACE SOMEDAY.

YOU MUST ACCEPT THAT YOU ARE NO LONGER A HUMAN.

...BUT THE OTHER HALF IS STILL HUMAN.

WAIT, DARREN!

GUU

GUU (ZZZ)

I CAN'T KEEP UP WITH MY CHANGING BODY. MY NAILS CUT SHARPER THAN ANY BLADE.

WE'VE TRAVELLED FAR IN THE TWO MONTHS SINCE I DIED.

IT SEEMS LIKE MOST OF THE THINGS I KNEW ABOUT VAMPIRES WERE FALSE.

IT'S NIGHT-TIME, MR. CREPS-LEY.

MR. CREPSLEY MADE FUN OF ME WHEN I ASKED WHY I HAD NO FANGS.

WELL, SORRY! THERE'S NO CAMPFIRE OR STOVE HERE.

CAN YOU NOT MAKE SOMETHING A BIT... NICER?

WHAT IS THIS!? SANDWICHES AGAIN!!?

GOOD MORNING, DARREN...

FUAAA CYAWND

YOU CAN ORDER ROOM SERVICE, THEN.

WE COULD HAVE HAD A CAMPFIRE, BUT YOU DID NOT WANT TO CAMP!

BUTSU

BUTSU (MUTTER)

SFX:PORI (SCRITCH) PORI

YES, I AM.

I ASSUME YOU ARE STILL SEEING TO MADAM OCTA.

NO! AN APPRENTICE PREPARES HIS MASTER'S FOOD!

HAGU (CHOMP)

HAGU

I THINK IT IS TIME I QUENCHED MY THIRST.

MAYBE YOU WILL JOIN ME THIS TIME.

BA (ZSHH)

...

MOGU (MUNCH)

MOGU MOGU

GARLIC DOESN'T HURT US, AND WE'RE NOT IMMORTAL.

WE'LL SEE ABOUT THAT...

VAMPIRES HAVE NOTHING TO FEAR FROM CROSSES OR HOLY WATER.

コト

KOTO (TOK)

THAT'S VAMPIRES FOR YOU.

WE'RE TOUGHER THAN NORMAL PEOPLE, BUT WE AREN'T INDESTRUCTIBLE.

A STAKE THROUGH THE HEART WOULD KILL US, OF COURSE, BUT SO WOULD A BULLET OR A KNIFE OR ELECTRICITY.

A VAMPIRE WOULDN'T DIE FROM SUNLIGHT IMMEDIATELY, BUT FOUR OR FIVE HOURS WOULD KILL HIM.

...BUT WE CAN'T BE PHOTOGRAPHED OR FILMED WITH A VIDEO CAMERA.

SOME OF THE MYTHS ARE TRUE, THOUGH. OUR REFLECTION CAN BE SEEN IN MIRRORS, AND WE CAST SHADOWS...

SFX: MUSHA (MUNCH) MUSHA

WAIT, WERE FROGS SAFE? I'LL HAVE TO ASK CREPSLEY AGAIN...

HAA (SIGH)

はぁ

DOGS AND COWS ARE SAFE TO DRINK, BUT NOT CATS OR SNAKES...

WE CAN'T DRINK JUST ANY ANIMAL'S BLOOD—SOME TYPES ARE POISONOUS TO US.

...THE VERY MAN WHO TURNED ME INTO A HALF-VAMPIRE.

TO BE HONEST, I HATE MR. CREPS-LEY...

THERE ARE SO MANY THINGS TO RE-MEMBER.

CARELESS HALF-VAMPIRES DON'T LAST VERY LONG.

I DREAM OF DRIVING A STAKE THROUGH HIS HEART AND PULLING THE CURTAINS ASIDE.

I COULD DO IT IF I WANTED.

I'M A HALF-VAMPIRE WITHOUT THE KNOWL-EDGE TO SURVIVE.

BUT I WON'T LAST WITHOUT HIS HELP.

NO USE STAYING PUT IN-DOORS ALL THE TIME.

I THINK I'LL GO INTO TOWN!

I DON'T HAVE TO WORRY ABOUT THE SUN.

BUT THERE ARE GOOD THINGS ABOUT BEING A HALF-VAMPIRE TOO.

SIGN: I'LL BE BACK IN A WHILE.

LET'S CHECK OUT THE TOWN!

PATAN (THUMP)

GAYA
カ"ア

GAYA
(YADDA)
カ"ア

PAPPAA
(BEEP
BEEP)

!!

AHH,
NOTHING LIKE
SOME GOOD
FRESH AIR!

MUM!
DAD!
ANNIE!!

IT
CAN'T
BE...

NO...

OH...

SORRY, MY MIS- TAKE...

?

I THOUGHT I HAD GIVEN UP ON THEM ...

SIGH... I CAN'T DO THIS...

HUP!

GET THE BALL FOR US!

HEY, YOU!

THEY WOULDN'T BE WALKING AROUND A FAR-OFF TOWN LIKE THIS...

KORO... (ROLL)

YES, YOU!

DO
(DMM)

WE'RE SHORT ONE PERSON!

WANNA PLAY WITH US?

AMAZING!

HOW'D HE DO THAT!?

HEY, YOU!

BAN
(WHAM)

WOW, YOU'RE GOOD!

YOU SURE LOOK FUNNY, THOUGH.

OH, I LOST MY BAG...

THESE ARE THE ONLY CLOTHES I HAVE LEFT.

BORO
(CRUMBLE)

MY NAME'S MICHAEL!

GYU
(SQUEEZE)

ギュッ

NICE TO MEET YOU!

I'M DARREN...

BEING A VAMPIRE DOESN'T MEAN YOU HAVE TO BE ALONE! I COULD FIND FRIENDS AGAIN AND...

MAN, THIS IS FUN! EVEN VAMPIRES CAN MAKE FRIENDS!

THAT'S A FOUL, DANNY!

WATCH OUT, DANNY PLAYS DIRTY.

WHAT'S HIS PROBLEM?

ZUN
(THUD)

I GOT IT!

BO
(CRAKK)

...MY BALL!!!

YOU OKAY, DARREN!?

IT'S MINE NOW!

...

WHY YOU...!

THAT WAS...

DA
(DSHH)

AAAAAGH!!

IT WAS AN ACCI-DENT...

N-NO! MICHAEL, I DIDN'T MEAN TO...

HIS FLESH IS RIPPED OPEN!

IS THAT A BONE?

AAAAH!!..

MONSTER!!!

STAY BACK!

KUAAA
(YAWWWN)

MMM, THAT IS A GOOD SMELL.

SU
(SHH)

ARE YOU READY TO EXPLAIN THINGS TO ME NOW?

......

SFX: FUUU (PUFF) FUUU

NIYARI (SMIRK)

I COULD GET USED TO THIS!

WHY DID WE HAVE TO LEAVE TOWN SO SUDDENLY?

WHAT HAP-PENED THIS AFTER-NOON?

YOU WILL JUST HAVE TO BE MORE CAREFUL NEXT TIME. BUT IT IS SOMETHING YOU MUST GET USED TO.

I SEE... AN UNFORTUNATE TALE.

I CAN'T HAVE FRIENDS ANYMORE. IF I DID, THEY WOULDN'T EVEN BE REAL FRIENDS.

NO. THERE WON'T BE A NEXT TIME. I'M TOO DANGEROUS.

HOW CAN YOU TELL A FRIEND, "OH, GUESS WHAT, I'M A VAMPIRE"?

BECAUSE TRUE FRIENDS DON'T KEEP SECRETS FROM ONE ANOTHER!

WHY IS THAT?

SURE, FRIENDS MIGHT NOT BE IMPORTANT TO ADULTS...

...THEY'VE GOT WORK AND HOBBIES TO KEEP THEM BUSY...

IS IT TRULY SO IMPORTANT TO YOU?

BUT IT IS A PROBLEM EVERY VAMPIRE SHARES!!

YOU COULD NEVER UNDERSTAND HOW I REALLY FEEL!!

...BUT MY FRIENDS WERE THE MOST IMPORTANT THING IN MY LIFE BESIDES MY FAMILY!!!

I AM SORRY, DARREN.

I SHOULD NOT HAVE BLOODED YOU. I DID NOT MAKE YOU A VAMPIRE TO HURT YOU. I...

HMM. WAIT A MINUTE...

IF YOU ARE NOT... "NORMAL," THEN...

NO MATTER HOW HARD YOU TRY TO BE NORMAL, YOU ARE NOT. THERE WILL ALWAYS BE ACCIDENTS WAITING TO HAPPEN.

WE ARE DIFFERENT FROM HUMANS...

...

WELL, THERE'S NO USE CRYING ABOUT IT...

IT WAS MY FAULT TO BEGIN WITH...

OF COURSE. YOU DO NOT HAVE TO BE STUCK WITH ME ALL THE TIME!

HA-HA! WHY DID I NOT THINK OF THIS EARLIER?

WHAT DO YOU MEAN?

DARREN, WHAT DO YOU THINK...

I AM NOT TALKING ABOUT HUMANS. I AM TALKING ABOUT PEOPLE WITH SPECIAL POWERS. PEOPLE LIKE US!

HUH?

WE CAN FIND FRIENDS FOR YOU, DARREN!

DIDN'T YOU SAY IT WASN'T SAFE FOR ME TO BE AROUND HUMANS?

...ABOUT GOING BACK AND BECOMING A MEMBER OF THE CIRQUE DU FREAK?

CHAPTER 6:
TO CIRQUE DU FREAK

MR. TALL, MR. TALL...

HMMM...

WE MUST BE GETTING QUITE CLOSE BY NOW.

AS IF I NEEDED YOU TO POINT THAT OUT!!

YOU'LL DIE IF YOU DON'T GET THERE BEFORE SUNRISE!

COME ON, SLOW-POKE!!

NOT EVEN TWO MILES AHEAD...

LET US MAKE HASTE.

ONCE I LOCATE THAT, FINDING CIRQUE DU FREAK'S LOCATION IS AS EASY AS FINDING A NEEDLE IN A HAYSTACK.

I WAS SEARCHING FOR MR. TALL'S AURA.

HA HA HA

WHAT WERE YOU DOING?

...LITTLE RAS-CAL...

I GET THE PIC-TURE!

I CAN'T DO IT BECAUSE I'M ONLY A HALF-VAMPIRE!

IS IT? ER...

THAT'S SUPPOSED TO BE HARD, ISN'T IT?

SFX: GOHON (AHEM)

OH, BUT YOU CANNOT DO THIS YET...

NOT FOR A VAM-PIRE!

ARE YOU READY TO PROCEED, DARREN?

ガサッ

GASA (RUSTLE)

I WAS EX-CITED, OF COURSE... BUT THAT WASN'T ALL.

...WOULD TRULY ACCEPT ME TO BE ONE OF THEIR OWN.

I STILL COULDN'T BE SURE THE CIRCUS...

WHAT IS WRONG? FEELING INSECURE?

...THEY'LL REALLY LET ME JOIN THE CIRQUE DU FREAK?

D-DO YOU THINK...

IF YOU DO NOT, THEN WE LEAVE. IT IS THAT SIMPLE.

IF YOU LIKE IT THERE, YOU MAY STAY.

...BUT THE REST IS UP TO YOU.

YOU WILL, OF COURSE, HAVE WORK TO DO THERE...

NOW, LET US PRO-CEED.

OH, IT'S YOU.

AAH!

KYORO (SPIN) KYORO

I THOUGHT I FELT YOU SEARCHING FOR ME...

... LARTEN CREPSLEY.

I SEE YOU'VE BROUGHT THE BOY.

NU CHRMM

WHAT IS IT ONE IS SUPPOSED TO SAY TO YOU VAMPIRES?

OF COURSE.

MAY WE COME IN?

HA HA HA

HA HA HA

HEH HEH HEH

SOMETHING LIKE THAT.

ENTER OF YOUR OWN FREE WILL...

... WAS IT?

SFX: NIYA (SMIRK)

ZURI ズリ (SCRAPE)

ZURI ズリ

I SEE...

NO, IT WAS FOR DARREN'S SAKE...

A SWIFT RETURN HAD NOT BEEN ON THE AGENDA, HIBERNIUS.

I DIDN'T EXPECT TO SEE YOU BACK SO SOON...
...LARTEN.

DID YOU RUN INTO TROUBLE?

HIBERNIUS? HIBERNIUS TALL? THAT'S A WEIRD NAME...

YOU HAVE COME A LONG WAY SINCE I SAW YOU LAST...
...DARREN SHAN.

ギ GISHI (CREAK)

ジ JI (STARE)

IS IT OKAY IF WE STAY?

YOU ARE LESS VALUABLE BUT WELCOME ALL THE SAME.

THANK YOU.

YOU AND MADAM OCTA WILL BE AN INVALUABLE ADDITION TO THE LINEUP.

OF COURSE. DELIGHTED TO HAVE YOU BACK, ACTUALLY. WE'RE UNDERSTAFFED AT THE MOMENT.

THIS SHOULD BE A GOOD CHANCE TO GET USED TO LIFE AMONG US.

WE WILL NOT PERFORM FOR THE NEXT FEW DAYS.

IT WILL BE NICE TO SLEEP IN IT ONCE MORE!

WONDERFUL! I HAVE MISSED IT SO.

YOUR COFFIN HAS BEEN WELL TAKEN CARE OF...

...LARTEN.

EVRA WOULD BE PERFECT...

PUT DARREN IN WITH ONE OF THE OTHER PERFORMERS. SOMEBODY HIS OWN AGE, IF POSSIBLE.

GATA (SHIVER)

GATA

WHAT ABOUT THE BOY? SHALL I HAVE ONE MADE FOR HIM TOO?

DON'T EVEN THINK ABOUT IT! YOU WON'T GET ME IN ONE OF THOSE AGAIN!

MY COF- MY COF- FIN. DEAR COF- FIN. ♪ ♪

HEY...

YOU WILL FIND OUT.

WHO'S EVRA?

GACHA (CLICK)

I HAVE TO BE AWAY IMMEDI- ATELY.

I WILL LEAVE DARREN WITH YOU, HIBER- NIUS.

SHALL WE BE GOING, THEN...?

BUT... WHO'S EVRA?

HE'S A BIT OLDER, BUT YOU TWO SHOULD GET ALONG JUST FINE.

I BELIEVE EVRA SHOULD BE WAKING SOON.

WHAT AM I TOUCHING?

SHURU (SLIDE)

UH, EXCUSE ME...

IT'S PITCH BLACK...

AAAAAHH!!

BIKU (TWITCH)

DOTA (THWOMP)

AH...

HEY, IT'S YOU!

JI (STARE)

...H-HEY, IS THIS A SNAKE? SNAKE!!!

S-SORRY, I D-DIDN'T MEAN TO...

JITA (SQUIRM)

BATA

WHAT IS GOING ON!?

WHAT IS IT!?

BATA (FLOP)

BATA

SHE WANTS TO KNOW IF YOU LIKE SAUSAGES OR IF YOU'RE A VEGETARIAN.

HUH? I DON'T...

BUT I'M STILL LEARNING.

I'M THE ONLY ONE IN THE CAMP WHO KNOWS WHAT TRUSKA'S SAYING.

NIKO (GRIN)

SHE'S NOT AT ALL LIKE SHE IS ON THE STAGE...

THE BEARDED WOMAN...

I LOVE SAUSAGES.

THANK YOU...

MORNIN', BOSS.

GOOD MORNING, MR. TALL!

GOOD MORNING, FRIENDS.

WELL, IT LOOKS LIKE YOU'RE FITTING IN, MASTER SHAN.

ZUI (LOON)

34

FOR THE MOMENT, STICK WITH EVRA AND HELP HIM WITH HIS CHORES.

...WE DON'T YET KNOW WHAT YOU ARE SUITED TO DO.

PERA (FLIP)

PERA

BY THE WAY, MASTER SHAN— ON THE SUBJECT OF TODAY'S WORK...

EVRA WILL BE IN CHARGE OF YOU UNTIL FURTHER NOTICE. DO WHAT HE SAYS.

PATAN (THUMP)

VERY WELL! IT'S SETTLED!

I'D LIKE THAT.

NOT AT ALL!

YOU DON'T MIND, EVRA?

NIKO (GRIN)

MY PLEA- SURE ...

TH- THANK YOU, MR. TALL!

WELL, DARREN...

SEE, DARREN, EVERYONE ELSE HERE IS LIKE YOU. WE'VE ALL GOT A STORY.

FINALLY, ONE DAY MR. TALL CAME TO THE RESCUE.

THEY BEAT ME AND TREATED ME LIKE A REAL SNAKE.

THEY KEPT ME LOCKED UP IN A GLASS CASE...

IT WAS A REALLY WICKED CIRCUS TOO.

THE FIRST THING I KNEW, I WAS IN A CIRCUS.

I'VE NEVER SEEN MY REAL PARENTS.

THERE'S NOTHING YOU NEED TO WORRY ABOUT ANYMORE!

DO YOU WANT TO SEE SOMETHING AMAZING?

WHOA, HEY! DID I SAY SOMETHING WRONG?

SNIFF... SNIFF...

COOL, HUH?

EWWW! GROSS!

CHECK THIS OUT!

BEROOON (BLIKK)

OH, STOP IT. THAT'S DISGUSTING.

HOJI (PICK) HOJI ほじ ほじ

I CAN EVEN PICK MY OWN NOSE!

MY NOSTRILS ARE THE CLEANEST PART OF MY WHOLE BODY.

THERE'S NO SNOT OR DIRT OR HAIRS!

MY NOSE IS DIFFERENT FROM YOURS.

ACTUALLY, IT'S NOT AT ALL.

IT'S THE SAME FLAVOUR AS THAT.

LICK MY SNAKE'S BELLY AND YOU'LL FIND OUT.

WHAT DOES IT TASTE LIKE?

YOU'RE ONE WEIRD GUY, KNOW THAT?

WHY NOT? YOU LOVE SPIDERS, DON'T YOU!?

NO WAY! I'M NOT THAT INTERESTED!

CHAPTER 7:
FRIEND NUMBER TWO

TODAY IS THE THIRD DAY SINCE I CAME TO THE CIRQUE.

I FEEL LIKE I'VE BEEN PART OF THE GROUP FOR YEARS.

I'VE COMPLETELY BLENDED IN WITH EVERY-DAY LIFE HERE.

GU (KRAK)

HRRGH!

GOT IT!

YOU GRAB THAT ONE, DARREN!

AND IT'S ALL THANKS TO EVRA.

SURE YOU'RE OKAY?

FURA

FURA (WOBBLE)

HUH!?

ZUSHI (OOMF)

I-I CAN H-HANDLE IT!

SO MUCH FOR THAT VAMPIRE STRENGTH!

FURA

BUT I DON'T CARE AT ALL ...

I CAN FEEL MY BODY WEAKENING BY THE DAY.

HALF OF MY VERY BEING IS SCREAMING OUT FOR THE LIFE-BEARING LIQUID.

I'M WEAK BECAUSE I WON'T DRINK HUMAN BLOOD.

I'D RATHER LOSE STRENGTH THAN DRINK ... ... FROM A HUMAN.

HMM?

HEY, EVRA...

SFX: BIKU (TWITCH)

?

GASA (RUSTLE)

COUGH, COUGH! ER, SEE YOU, EVRA!

AHEM! I'M LEAVING, DARREN! SEE YOU LATER!

WHAT, REALLY?

GONYO (WHISPER)

GONYO

NO, DON'T LOOK!

...

...

WWOOOH!!!

BIKU (BOING)

AAAH!!

HEE HEE HEE!

WRAAARGH!!

OOPS.

PATAN
(THUD)

SFX: CHIRO (FLICK) CHIRO

FURA
(FLOP)

I'LL GO CALL FOR HELP!

GA
(SNATCH)

SFX: SHIIN (SHHH)

ARE YOU ALL RIGHT? WAKE UP!

HE FAINTED! KID, ARE YOU OKAY!?

I KNEW YOU WERE WITH SOME KIND OF CIRCUS!

BUT A FREAK SHOW IS EVEN BETTER!

YUM!

HEY...

MY FAVOU-RITE!

THEY'RE PICKLED ONIONS.

CKLED NIONS

YOU MUST BE THE LUCKIEST GUYS ON THE PLANET!

IT'S SO COOL!

OH, SORRY. WANT ONE?

YOUR SCALES ARE PARTICU-LARLY FASCINAT-ING, EVRA.

SFX: PORI (MUNCH) PORI

I'M A HARD WORKER, AND I'M REALLY SMART! I'M SERIOUS!

COME ON, I'M NOT JOKING!

HA HA HA!

HA HA HA!

COULD YOU HELP ME JOIN?

MY PARENTS WOULD BE DELIGHTED FOR ME!

THEY THINK TRAVEL BROADENS THE MIND. I COULD SEE MAR-VELLOUS, MYSTICAL SIGHTS!

BAN (BOOM)

BUT YOU GUYS ARE KIDS TOO!!

I DON'T THINK SO, SAM. WE DON'T TAKE ON KIDS.

AND WHAT WOULD YOUR PARENTS THINK?

WELL, WE'RE NOT EXACTLY... NORMAL, SEE?

SCHOOL IS JUST A SYSTEM DESIGNED TO CRUSH THE SPIRIT AND STAMP OUT CREATIVITY!!

WHAT ABOUT SCHOOL, THEN?

...

SORRY, MAYBE WHEN YOU'RE OLDER.

SO, AM I IN? ARE WE COOL?

HE'S GOT AN ANSWER FOR EVERY-THING...

WE HAVE UNLIMITED POSSIBILITIES!

WE SHOULD BE FREE TO DO WHAT WE WANT!

DOES THAT MEAN KIDS AREN'T ALLOWED TO DO ANYTHING?

PEOPLE ALWAYS SAY "WHEN YOU'RE OLDER"!

IT'S NOT FAIR!

KIDS ARE ALWAYS FORCED TO FOLLOW ADULTS' ORDERS!

BUWA (RAAGH)

ENOUGH, SAM!

OKAY!

WE'RE NOT MEANT TO BE SLAVES! WE'RE —!

WE HAVE DESIRES AND GOALS!

WE HAVE WILLS OF OUR OWN!

...

DO YOU WANT TO COME SEE MY SNAKE?

PAA (GLOW)

PROO

HA HA...

C'MON, LET'S GO! HURRY!

I THOUGHT YOU'D NEVER ASK!

TA (TMP)

DO I? ARE YOU KIDDING?

ANY-
THING,
HUH...

...TO
KEEP
MADAM
OCTA FOR
A PET!

I'D DO
ANY-
THING
...

I'D DO
ANY-
THING
TO BE
IN YOUR
PLACE!

MAN, THIS
IS THE
GREATEST!
YOU GUYS
ARE SO
LUCKY!

PIKU
(TWITCH)

PASA
(FLAP)

INSIDE HERE IS THE WOLF-MAN'S TENT.

GURURU RURURU (GRRRRRRR)

JARA (CLANK)

UGH, WHAT A SMELL...

WHAT'S WRONG? DON'T YOU WANT A CLOSER LOOK?

WE'D BE IN DANGER IF WE DIDN'T...

ISN'T IT CRUEL?

WHY IS ONLY THE WOLF-MAN CHAINED UP?

THERE ISN'T A CURE BECAUSE IT ISN'T A DISEASE—HE WAS BORN THAT WAY.

ISN'T THERE A CURE?

HOW DID IT HAPPEN?

...HE'D RUN FREE AND KILL PEOPLE.

THE MIXED HUMAN AND WOLF BLOOD MEANS...

DO YOU REALLY WANT TO KNOW?

NUH-UH...

I'M SCARED...

GAAAA (RAWWWR)

DON'T YOU THINK?

IT'S GETTING DARK, SAM.

YOU OUGHT TO BE GETTING BACK HOME SOON.

POSITIVE. I PROMISE!

YOU'RE SURE THE CIRQUE WON'T HAVE MOVED AWAY BY THEN?

......

......

DO YOU WANT TO COME OVER IN THE AFTERNOON AND HANG OUT WITH US?

WHAT ABOUT TOMORROW?

NOT A PROBLEM.

THANKS FOR SHOWING ME AROUND, EVRA!

IT'S A PROMISE!

OKAY, TOMORROW AFTERNOON IT IS, THEN!

WE'RE FRIENDS, RIGHT?

IT'S A SIGN OF FRIENDSHIP!

THANKS, DARREN!

YEAH!

THIS IS OUR PLACE, HERE AT THE CIRQUE.

EVERYONE HAS THEIR PLACE IN THE WORLD. THE PLACE THEY'RE MEANT TO BE.

BUT I DON'T THINK IT'S WHERE SAM IS MEANT TO BE HAPPY.

A BIT CHEEKY, THOUGH.

SAM'S A GOOD GUY, ISN'T HE?

NOT REALLY...

DO YOU THINK HE'D FIT IN IF HE DID JOIN THE SHOW?

THIS PLACE ISN'T ALL JUST FUN AND GAMES.

REMEMBER WHAT MR. TALL SAID?

JUST DON'T SPOIL HIM, OKAY?

I MEAN, NOT THAT I KNOW EVERYTHING!

FRIENDS...

THAT'S FRIEND NUMBER TWO!

GYU (SQUEEZE)

WE'RE FRIENDS, RIGHT?

GATA

GATA (SHIVER)

EVRA...?

OTHERWISE I WOULDN'T HAVE MET YOU OR SAM OR—

I'M GLAD I CAME BACK TO JOIN THE CIRQUE DU FREAK!

BUT YOU KNOW WHAT, EVRA?

CHAPTER 8:
MR. TINY

EVEN MR. TALL GETS FIDGETY WHEN MR. TINY'S AROUND.

THE OTHER MEMBERS OF THE CIRQUE FEEL THE SAME WAY. NOBODY LIKES HIM.

MR. TINY IS THE SPOOKIEST MAN I'VE EVER MET.

...EVERY TIME HE LOOKS AT ME, I JUST GET SO TERRIFIED...

IT'S HARD TO EX-PLAIN, BUT...

WHAT COULD HE WANT THIS TIME?

IT'S BEEN TWO YEARS SINCE I LAST SAW HIM.

SFX: GATA (TREMBLE) GATA

SEEMS MR. TINY WANTS YOU TWO...

MR. TALL WANTS YOU TO REPORT TO HIS TRAILER AS SOON AS POSSIBLE.

EVRA, DARREN...

PASA (FLAP)

H-HERE WE ARE ...

LISTEN TO ME, DARREN. NO MATTER WHAT HE SAYS, DON'T TALK BACK TO MR. TINY.

JUST DO IT!

KON (KNOCK) KON

BUT ...

JUST SAY "YES, SIR," AND STAY QUIET.

KOCHI (TOCK)

KACHI (TICK)

AND...

... EVRA VON.

AH, SO GOOD OF YOU TO COME...

A WATCH...

...IN THE SHAPE OF A HEART.

I'VE BEEN HEARING A LOT ABOUT YOU, YOUNG FELLOW!

AH, YOU MUST BE DARREN SHAN!

SFX: GASHI (SNATCH)

PLEASE! NONE OF THAT STUFFINESS.

...MR. DESMOND TINY.

NO, I'M NO HERO...

A MOST REMARKABLE YOUNG MAN...

SACRIFICED EVERYTHING TO SAVE A FRIEND...

...LARTEN TELLS ME YOU'RE RELUCTANT TO DRINK HUMAN BLOOD.

BY THE WAY, DARREN...

DES DESTINY...

DESTINY...

ALL RIGHT, DES...

"DESTINY"...

YOU CAN CALL ME DES.

WHAT'S WRONG WITH THAT?

THEIR BLOOD IS SCRUMP-DILLY-ICIOUS!

APART FROM YOUNG CHILDREN, OF COURSE.

I DON'T BLAME YOU. NASTY, REPULSIVE STUFF.

SO!?

IF THEY'RE YOUNG ENOUGH, THEY COULD DIE...

YOU CAN'T DRINK BLOOD FROM THEM. THEY'RE TOO YOUNG.

ZAWA (DSHH)

MAINLY I WANT YOU TO FIND FOOD FOR THEM.

I'D APPRECIATE IT IF YOU WOULD HELP ME LOOK AFTER THEM.

DOWN TO BUSINESS!

BUT ENOUGH ABOUT THAT!

SFX: GISHI (CREAK)

MY BLUE-ROBED MINIONS.

YOU SAW ME ARRIVE WITH MY LITTLE PEOPLE.

KYU (WIPE)

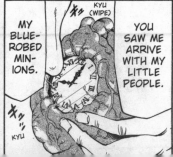

KYU

NORMALLY I'D STICK AROUND AND SEE TO IT MYSELF, BUT I HAVE BUSINESS ELSEWHERE.

THEY HAVE SUCH BIG APPE- TITES.

I'VE ALREADY GOT THE PERMISSION OF YOUR GUARD- IANS.

HOW ABOUT IT, BOYS?

EX- CEL- LENT!

YOUNG EVRA VON KNOWS WHAT MY DARLINGS LIKE, I'M SURE.

YOU MAY BEGIN TOMORROW MORNING.

W-WE'LL DO IT, SIR...

KOKU (NOD)

COME ON, DARREN.

LET'S GO!

MARQUE'D FREAK

YOU MAY GO.

WE'RE DONE HERE.

SFX:SHI (SHOO) SHI

GOOD NIGHT, SIR...

...WHY YOU CALL THEM LITTLE PEOPLE?

...BUT CAN YOU EXPLAIN TO ME...

EXCUSE ME...

DON'T THEY EACH HAVE INDIVIDUAL NAMES!?

DON'T THEY HAVE ANY OTHER NAMES?

STOP IT, DARREN!

WHY?

BE-CAUSE THEY ARE LITTLE.

IT'S VERY IMPORTANT!

UNDER-STAND EACH OTHER? SUCH A LAUGH-ABLE CON-CEPT.

HOW CAN THEY UNDER-STAND EACH OTHER?

HOW CAN YOU LIVE YOUR LIFE WITHOUT KNOWING YOUR OWN NAME?

YOU'RE WRONG! THEY DO!

THEY DON'T EACH NEED THEIR OWN NAMES.

BIKU (TWITCH)

I HEARD YOU WERE A PEST, BUT NOBODY TOLD ME YOU WERE THIS NOSY.

GATA (THUMP)

I DON'T MEAN TO BE RUDE, SIR. I JUST...

PITA (STOP)

I DON'T LIKE THIS INSOLENCE...

KYU (WIPE) KYU

WELL, THIS BIRD HAD BETTER LEARN TO KEEP HIS BEAK SHUT...

ALL THIS CHIRPING AND TWITTERING, JUST LIKE A LITTLE BIRD.

WHY DON'T YOU MAKE ME?

I CAN'T BACK DOWN NOW...

SFX: GOKU (GULP)

DARREN...

...SHAN...

KA (FLASH)

SFX: GYUUU (SQUEEZE)

66

URGH...

ZUKUN
(GRGG)

GYUU

BASA
(FLAP)

PERHAPS THE THEATRE. NO, THE BRIDGE...

HAVE WE MET BEFORE?

COME ON!

YOU COULD USE PLENTY OF SLEEP TONIGHT.

NO STUDIES—STRAIGHT TO BED.

...THIS IS OUR FIRST MEETING, SIR.

NO...

WAIT, DARREN SHAN!

YOU MUST BE OUT OF YOUR MIND!

ARE YOU CRAZY? TALKING BACK TO MR. TINY LIKE THAT!

SOMETHING BLACK AND EVIL...

I FELT SOMETHING TRULY AWFUL EMANATING FROM THAT MAN.

AHH, GEEZ!

YOU'RE RIGHT, I MUST BE.

I HAD THAT FEELING.

BUT I COULD TELL THAT YOU AND EVERYONE ELSE... WERE TERRIFIED.

IT'S A MONUMENTAL TASK JUST TO PREPARE THEIR FOOD.

THEY REALLY DO EAT A LOT.

MR. TINY LEFT THE CIRQUE DU FREAK THAT NIGHT...

...AND THE NEXT MORNING OUR PERIOD OF SERVICE TO THE LITTLE PEOPLE BEGAN.

EVRA SAYS HE'S NEVER SEEN THEM SPEAK, EVER.

BAKU (MUNCH)

GUA (GOBBLE)

GA (CHOMP)

THEY DON'T SPEAK A WORD—JUST EAT IN SILENCE.

LET ME TELL YOU, I'M TOTALLY WORN OUT...

YOU LOOK RATHER PALE, DARREN. ARE YOU OKAY?

WOW, THAT SOUNDS TOUGH.

AND THERE ARE TWELVE OF THEM, RIGHT?

I DON'T THINK I CAN LAST MUCH LONGER ON ANIMAL BLOOD...

FURA...

NU (NRRG)

GIRO (GLARE)

THAT WAS A LIE.

CASA (RUSTLE)

I'M FINE. I'M ALWAYS LIKE THIS.

HOW MANY MONTHS HAS IT BEEN WITHOUT HUMAN BLOOD?

FURA (WOBBLE)

I'VE BEEN LOSING STRENGTH STEADILY, EVERY DAY.

HE'S HUGE!

WELL? ARE YOU SUR-PRISED!?

HA HA HA HA!!

GOTCHA!!

YOU MUST BE DARREN, THEN! I'M SAM'S FRIEND! NAME'S REGGIE VEGGIE.

BUT YOU CAN CALL ME R.V.

I TOLD HIM TO HIDE IN THE BUSHES SO HE COULD SCARE YOU GUYS!

I MET R.V. ON THE WAY OVER HERE!

IT'S GOOD STUFF!

TOMA-TOES AND BEANS!

EAT UP, MAN. YOU LOOK PEAKY.

HEH HEH!

YOU SURE LOVE YOUR SCARES, DON'T YOU, SAM?

HE FIGHTS TO PROTECT NATURE AND ANIMALS!

A WARRIOR, HUH? SOUNDS COOL.

THAT'S WHY HE DOESN'T EAT MEAT!

R.V.'S AN ECO-WARRIOR!

THANKS.

HE'S TAUGHT ME ALL SORTS OF THINGS!

AND HE LIVES WITHOUT RELYING ON A CIVILIZATION BUILT ON NATURAL DESTRUCTION!

YOU GUYS ARE HERE WITH THE CIRCUS, RIGHT?

HA-HA! HECK, ALL I'M DOING IS LIVING BY MY BELIEFS, MAN.

IT'S LIKE OUR HOME THERE. WE'RE ALL A BIG FAMILY.

NO, NOT AT ALL.

THEY DON'T WHIP YOU OR UNDERFEED YOU OR ANYTHING LIKE THAT?

THEY DON'T MISTREAT YOU, DO THEY?

YEAH, THAT'S RIGHT. THE FREAK SHOW.

SFX: JI (STARE)

OH. THAT'S OKAY, THEN...

I'LL THINK ABOUT IT.

RIGHT, DARREN?

COME AND SEE THE CIRQUE, IF YOU FEEL LIKE IT.

YEAH, THANKS A LOT!

THANKS FOR THE FOOD, R.V.

WELL, WE SHOULD BE GOING.

BYE, BYE!

I CAN RESPECT THE SACRIFICE HE MAKES!

IT'S PRETTY WEIRD. I COULDN'T DO THAT.

IMAGINE GIVING UP EVERYTHING TO FIGHT FOR THE EARTH!

THERE SURE ARE SOME INTERESTING PEOPLE OUT THERE.

ZA CZSHHHH

ZA

ZA

SFX: SURA (SLIP)

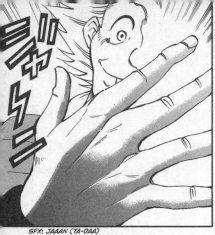

SFX: JAAAN (TA-DAA)

NYU (POIK)

NYU

MUNYU (SPROIT)

WHO KNOWS WHAT COULD HAPPEN? WOULDN'T WANT TO TEMPT FATE.

THE ONLY THING I HAVEN'T TRIED YET IS MY HEAD.

I CAN GROW NEW LIMBS— ARMS, LEGS, ANYTHING—IN A MATTER OF SECONDS!

SFX: GU (SQUEEZE) SFX: PA (FLICK)

THIS IS NO TIME FOR DIS- CUSSION!

PAN

PAN (CLAP)

COME, COME!!

...HAVE REJOINED OUR PRO- DUCTION!

CORMAC LIMBS AND LARTEN CREPSLEY...

CHAPTER 9:
A TINY URGE TO KILL

GOOD! THINGS ARE LOOKING SPICK-AND-SPAN...

ALL THAT'S LEFT IS FOR THE GUESTS TO ARRIVE.

SAM!!

BUT...

YOUR FAMILY WILL WORRY, WON'T THEY?

MUSU (CHMPH)

WHAT? NO, I'M FINE!

YOU OUGHT TO HEAD HOME.

THANKS FOR THE HELP, SAM. IT'S GOING TO BE DARK SOON.

HANG ON JUST A MINUTE, SAM!

TA (TSHH)

OH...

SHEESH!

GEEZ!

 **WHAT IS IT, DAR-REN?**

FUU (WHEW)

 **OKAY, SAM!**

 **HERE! TAKE THEM!**

TICKETS: CIRQUE DU FREAK

 **NO PROBLEM. THE ONLY THING IS, IT'S A LATE SHOW.**

OH, WOW! THANKS, DAR-REN!!

 **ONE FOR YOU AND ONE FOR R.V.**

TICKETS FOR TONIGHT'S SHOW.

ARE THESE WHAT I THINK THEY ARE?

 **I'VE GOT TO GO HAND ONE OF THESE TO R.V.!**

SURE! I'LL SNEAK OUT. MUM AND DAD GO TO BED AT NINE EVERY NIGHT. THEY'RE EARLY BIRDS.

WE'RE STARTING AT ELEVEN, AND IT WON'T BE OVER TILL NEARLY ONE IN THE MORNING. WILL YOU BE ABLE TO COME?

THERE'S NOTHING WRONG WITH HIM SEEING THE SHOW, RIGHT?

I BEGGED MR. TALL FOR SOME EXTRAS.

WHERE'D THE TICKETS COME FROM?

THANKS SO MUCH! SEE YOU TONIGHT!

...HE JUST CAN'T BE HONEST, CAN HE?

HMM...

...AND I WOULD LIKE HIM TO SEE MY SHOW. BUT STILL...

I GUESS NOT. HE WORKED PRETTY HARD FOR US TODAY...

COME WITH ME, DARREN.

THEN BRUSH YOUR SUIT DOWN AND CLEAN YOURSELF UP.

POLISH MADAM OCTA'S CAGE.

BASA (FLAP)

I KNOW THAT ...

I KNOW THAT!

I AM SPEAKING FOR YOUR OWN SAKE, DARREN...

LET'S NOT TALK ABOUT THIS!

SOME DAY, YOU WILL ...

YOU MIGHT THINK YOU ARE MAKING DO WITH ANIMAL BLOOD, BUT IT WILL NOT LAST!

WAA (OOOH)

THE CIRQUE STARTED AT ELEVEN O'CLOCK ON THE DOT.

JUST MAKE SURE YOU ARE READY TO...

NO, NEVER MIND...

82

WE WERE OUT IN THE COUNTRY WITH BARELY ANY TIME FOR ADVERTISE-MENT, BUT THE TENT WAS PACKED FULL.

ACCORDING TO EVRA, PEOPLE ALWAYS KNOW WHEN OUR SHOWS ARE HAPPENING, AND THEY COME FROM EVERY-WHERE, SO THIS WAS NO SURPRISE.

...I'D BE A MEMBER OF THE CIRCUS I ONCE SAW?

WOW

HOW COULD I HAVE KNOWN THAT ONE DAY...

KYU (TIE)

YOU WERE AWE-SOME, EVRA!

HOW WAS IT, DARREN?

YEAH!

IS EVERYTHING READY?

WE ARE UP NEXT.

DOKI (BA-BUMP) DOKI

DON'T LET YOUR NERVES GET TO YOU!

SHE SAYS HANG IN THERE!

Up next, we have a most fascinating pair!

I present to you, Mr. Crepsley...

...And his performing spider, Madam Octa!!

SHE IS BOTH POISONOUS AND INTELLIGENT...

MADAM OCTA IS TRULY AN INCREDIBLE SPIDER.

KYORO (SPIN) KYORO

IT'S SO BRIGHT!

AHA!

BA!
(LEAP)

R.V.!

SAM!

...BUT I WILL LET YOU WITNESS HER TERROR FOR YOUR-SELVES.

ZORO
(CREEP)

THEY'RE TOTALLY AMAZED!

GABU
(CHOMP)

ZAZAZA
(SCUTTLE)

IF YOU DO, SHE WILL COME AFTER ME...

BE CAREFUL NOT TO MAKE ANY LOUD NOISES.

OF COURSE, A HUMAN BEING WOULD NOT LAST AN INSTANT.

GASA
(SCUTTLE)
GASA

YOU WILL HAVE TO CONTROL MADAM OCTA NOW.

NOW I'M REALLY FEELING NERVOUS...

BE CAREFUL.

EVERY-ONE IN THE ENTIRE AUDIENCE IS WATCHING ME...

SAM... R.V....

SFX: KURA (SWOON)

IF I LOSE MY CON-CENTRATION DURING THE ACT...

..IT'LL BE THE SAME THING AS BE-FORE...

CONCEN-TRATE! GOT TO CONCEN-TRATE. I'M CONTROLLING MADAM OCTA RIGHT NOW!

I CAN FEEL MYSELF PHASING OUT...EVEN AFTER ALL THE ANIMAL BLOOD I DRANK BEFORE THE SHOW...

THAT SAME NIGHTMARE ALL OVER AGAIN!

KATA
(SHIVER)
KATA

HOW COULD I FORGET?

YES, JUST LIKE THEN...

THIS IS MY CHANCE...

GASHIN
(CRASH!!)

...MY GREATEST OPPOR-TUNITY TO FINALLY ACCOM-PLISH WHAT I SWORE TO DO...

...KILL MR. CREPSLEY!!!

BUT I'VE NEVER TRULY PLOTTED HOW TO DO IT.

I'VE WANTED TO KILL HIM BEFORE.

JUST "KILL MR. CREPSLEY"...

IT WOULD JUST BE ONE LITTLE COMMAND TO MADAM OCTA.

KARI (SCRAPE)

ESPECIALLY NOT SINCE WE CAME BACK HERE TO THE CIRQUE DU FREAK...

HAPPY WITH MY LIFE HERE?

HAVE I BEEN SATIS- FIED?

I LOST MY HUMANITY, MY FRIENDS, MY FAMILY— EVERYTHING.

AND WHOSE FAULT WAS IT!?

YES... BUT DON'T FOR- GET!

!

DO IT! THIS IS IT, DARREN!

NOW'S YOUR—

NOT EVEN MR. CREPSLEY COULD DEFEND HIMSELF AGAINST HER NOW!

IF THERE'S ANY MOMENT TO DO IT, IT'S NOW.

NIYARI (SMIRK)

GABA (LURCH)

HAGU (CHOMP)

WHY WOULD I—?

HE'S EVEN DONE HIS BEST TO BE NICE TO ME...IN HIS OWN WAY.

...BUT THE ONLY REASON I'M ON STAGE NOW IS BECAUSE OF MR. CREPSLEY.

AND THE REASON I MET EVRA AND SAM TOO...

TSU
(CHANG)

FRESH SPIDER-WEBS ARE A TREAT WHERE I COME FROM!!

DELICIOUS! NOTHING TASTIER!

WA (COOOH)

...ABOUT KILLING ME OUT THERE, DID YOU NOT?

YOU THOUGHT...

I JUST CAN'T KILL MR. CREPSLEY... I CAN'T...

I CAN'T DO IT...

!!!

...IT WAS JUST A TEST!? YOU WERE LOOKING TO SEE WHAT I'D DO!?

THEN...

IT WOULD NOT HAVE WORKED. I MILKED MOST OF THE POISON FROM HER FANGS BEFORE WE WENT ON.

KILLING THE GOAT TOOK THE REST OUT OF HER.

H-HOW DID YOU KNOW THAT?

YOU HAVE NOT ACCEPTED THE CORE FACT OF BEING A VAMPIRE. I HAD TO KNOW IF I COULD TRULY TRUST YOU...

YOU HAVE NEVER TAKEN HUMAN BLOOD.

I HAD TO BE SURE, DARREN.

...AND ALL THIS TIME, IT WAS JUST A TEST... NOTHING MORE...

I THOUGHT YOU WERE BEING NICE TO ME...

IT WAS THE ONLY WAY I COULD THINK OF...

THAT IS WHY I HAD YOU COME ON STAGE.

THAT IS COR-RECT.

...MR. CREPS-LEY? WHAT'S WRONG WITH DARREN...

HEY, DAR-REN! GOOD JOB ON YOUR FIRST...

AAH!

NEVER EVER!!

I'LL NEVER DRINK HUMAN BLOOD!

I CAN'T BELIEVE IT...

...EVEN IF I DIDN'T ACT LIKE A VAMPIRE...

EVEN IF I DIDN'T DRINK HUMAN BLOOD...

HOW COULD HE DO SUCH A THING...?

...HE MIGHT BE OKAY, AFTER ALL...

...I THOUGHT...

KEEP OUT

CHAPTER 10:
A CONDITION FOR SAM

CHICHI
(CHIRP)

CHICHICHI
(TWEET)

YOU THOUGHT ABOUT...

...KILLING ME OUT THERE...

...DID YOU NOT?

BUT EVEN THEN, HE SHOULDN'T HAVE TESTED ME THAT WAY...

CREPSLEY WAS RIGHT... THIS IS ALL ULTIMATELY MY FAULT.

IF IT HAPPENS, I REALLY WILL BE A TRUE VAMPIRE FOR GOOD.

I JUST CAN'T DRINK HUMAN BLOOD... I DON'T WANT TO.

MMMG!!!

AAAHH!!

AHH!!

DO) (SHOVE)

SFX: GA (CRUNCH)

(DOSA (THWAM)

MR. CREPS-LEY!?

ZEE (WHEEZE) ZEE

GEHO (COUGH) GEHO

SHUT UP!!

IF YOU GO ON LIKE THIS, YOU WILL BE DEAD WITHIN A WEEK!

THAT IS RIGHT! I WAS GOING TO MAKE YOU DRINK IT BY FORCE!

...IT'S WHAT YOU KEEP HUMAN BLOOD IN...

THAT BOTTLE...

GU... CRRGH

YOU WERE TRYING TO GET ME TO DRINK!

JUST TRY THAT STUNT AGAIN!

NEXT TIME I REALLY WILL KILL YOU!

YOU MIGHT HAVE SURVIVED LAST NIGHT...

...BUT NOT NEXT TIME!!

YOU HAVE LIVED A GOOD LIFE.

VERY WELL. IF YOU FEEL SO STRONGLY, I WILL NOT BRING IT UP AGAIN...

THE VAMPIRE GODS WILL ACCEPT YOU.

KURA CSWOOND

AAGH...

DAR- REN...

URGH...

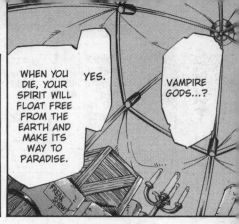

VAMPIRE GODS...?

YES.

WHEN YOU DIE, YOUR SPIRIT WILL FLOAT FREE FROM THE EARTH AND MAKE ITS WAY TO PARADISE.

HA-HA! GODS? PARADISE?

A VAMPIRE WHO DRINKS HUMAN BLOOD, LIVING A GOOD LIFE? IMPOSSIBLE...

DRINKING BLOOD IS NOT AN EVIL ACT IN ITSELF...

...NOT UNLESS YOU KILL THE PERSON YOU DRINK FROM.

AND EVEN THEN, SOMETIMES IT CAN BE A GOOD THING.

KILLING SOMEONE CAN BE GOOD?

WHEN A VAMPIRE DRAINS A PERSON'S BLOOD...

...HE ABSORBS SOME OF THAT PERSON'S MEMORIES AND FEELINGS.

IT IS A SPECIAL RITUAL THAT CAN ONLY BE DONE...

...AT THE REQUEST OF A PERSON WHO IS CLOSE TO DEATH.

...AND REMEMBER THINGS WHICH MIGHT OTHERWISE HAVE BEEN FORGOTTEN.

...AND WE SEE THE WORLD THE WAY THEY SAW IT...

THEIR SPIRIT BECOMES PART OF OUR FLESH AND BLOOD...

SO YOU SEE, IT IS A VERY GOOD THING AFTER ALL.

...BUT I WANT YOU TO KNOW THAT I WAS TRYING TO DO YOU A FAVOUR.

I WILL NOT ORDER YOU TO DRINK BLOOD...

HUH ...?

...I WILL NOT STOP YOU FROM LEAV- ING.

BUT IF YOU TRULY WANT TO BE FREE OF ME...

I CANNOT DO THAT... THOUGH SOMETIMES I WISH I COULD.

FORGET ABOUT ME...

JUST LEAVE ME ALONE ...

THAT WAY, YOU WOULD NO LONGER BE MY RESPONSIBILITY...

REALLY, I DO NOT MIND. IN FACT, I WOULD PREFER IT IF YOU DID.

AND IF YOU DO EVENTUALLY DIE...

...I WOULD NOT HAVE TO WATCH IT.

I CANNOT READ MINDS, BOY.

IF ONLY I COULD READ MINDS THE WAY YOU CAN.

I HAVE NO IDEA WHAT YOU'RE THINKING SOME- TIMES...

FIRST YOU ACT NICE, THEN YOU PUSH ME AWAY...

YOU WERE JUST THAT EASY TO FIGURE OUT.

I AM NOT MR. TALL.

...WHEN YOU TURNED ME INTO A VAMPIRE, AND AFTER YESTERDAY'S ACT...

HUH? BUT...

I CANNOT UNDERSTAND A THING YOU ARE THINKING, EITHER.

IF I COULD READ YOUR MIND, I WOULD NOT BE HAVING THIS TROUBLE...

HEH HEH...

HA...

I'LL FIX YOU SOME-THING. HANG ON A MOMENT.

NO, DARREN. I AM NOT HUNGRY.

GUUUU (GURRRGLE)

NUAAH!!

THE SUN'S STILL OUT, SO I'LL GO AND MAKE YOU SOME FOOD.

YOU HAVEN'T EATEN SINCE LAST NIGHT, HAVE YOU?

DARREN!!

...I RECOGNIZE THAT HE IS CONCERNED FOR ME AND TRYING TO HELP.

I CAN'T DRINK HUMAN BLOOD UNDER ANY CIRCUM-STANCES, BUT...

A LITTLE SALTY...

I'LL TRUST MR. CREPS-LEY FOR NOW.

HE ALSO DIDN'T LIKE THE PARTS WITH EVRA'S SNAKE AND MADAM OCTA...

I THINK HE WAS A LITTLE UPSET ABOUT THAT...

YOU KNOW THE PART OF YOUR ACT WHERE THE GOAT DIED?

REALLY?

NO, I'M SURE HE DID...

I THINK HE ENJOYED IT...

...BUT MOST OF ALL, HE COULDN'T STAND THE WOLF-MAN BEING LOCKED IN THAT CAGE...

BURU (SHIVER)

BURU

I GUESS ...

HMM, WELL ...

HE RISKS HIS LIFE TO FIGHT FOR ANIMALS AND THE ENVIRONMENT!

OF COURSE! R.V.'S AN ECOLOGICAL WARRIOR...

I'VE MADE UP MY MIND FOR GOOD!

AND I WOULDN'T HAVE SEEN IT WITHOUT YOUR TICKET!

OH, BUT I LIKED EVERY PART OF THE SHOW!

THAT WAS A BAD IDEA...

WE'RE FRIENDS, AREN'T WE?

NOTHING... BUT THIS ISN'T SOMETHING I CAN DECIDE ON MY OWN.

THEN TALK TO THE OWNER...

PUT IN A GOOD WORD WITH MR. TALL FOR ME! PLEASE!

REALLY!? WHEN, WHEN!?

BUT BEFORE WE GO TO MR. TALL, I'LL CHECK WITH MR. CREPSLEY FIRST.

OKAY, SAM, I'LL ASK.

THANK YOU!!

THANK YOU, DARREN!

HANG ON A MINUTE.

I'LL ASK RIGHT NOW.

PAA (GLOW)

MAYBE IT'S BECAUSE OF ALL THE FOOD I'VE BEEN MAKING FOR THE LITTLE PEOPLE.

DELICIOUS! I DO BELIEVE YOU HAVE LEARNED A THING OR TWO SINCE WE CAME HERE!

HERE'S YOUR FOOD.

I KNOW.

HE'S BEEN HELPING EVRA AND ME WITH OUR CHORES.

SO I HAVE HEARD.

HE'S A GOOD WORKER.

...WHAT DO YOU THINK OF SAM?

MR. CREPSLEY...

BUT HE SEEMS NICE. VERY BRIGHT.

I HAVE NOT SEEN MUCH OF HIM. HE COMES MOSTLY BY DAY.

GIRO (GLARE)

...HE WANTS TO JOIN THE CIRQUE.

WELL...

109

CHILDREN CANNOT JOIN UNLESS AN INDEPENDENT MEMBER AGREES TO BE THEIR GUARDIAN.

HE WILL SAY YOU HAVE TO ASK ME.

WHAT DO YOU THINK HE'LL SAY?

I WAS GOING TO ASK MR. TALL, BUT IT'S STILL A LITTLE EARLY TO BRING IT UP.

HE'S MY FRIEND. PLEASE, YOU MUST!

BESIDES, HE IS HUMAN.

THEN YOU COULD BE HIS GUARDIAN...

I WILL NOT TAKE ON A SECOND.

ABSOLUTELY NOT. ONE CHILD IS BAD ENOUGH.

YOU THINK HE WILL UNDERSTAND?

WHAT HAPPENS WHEN HE FINDS OUT YOU ARE A VAMPIRE?

OH? TELL ME THIS.

KARAN (CLANG)

110

 Y-YOU DON'T KNOW THAT...

 HUMANS AND VAMPIRES WILL NEVER CO-EXIST.

WE ARE NOT LIKE HUMANS...

 DARREN, YOU HAVE NOT FORGOTTEN THE LOOKS OF HATRED AND MISTRUST YOU RECEIVED.

 Y-YOU WON'T LET HIM JOIN?

 BUT ON ONE CONDITION.

 YOU WILL!?

I CAN GO TO MR. TALL AND TELL HIM THAT I AM TAKING HIM IN...

GATA (THUMP)

 VERY WELL, HE CAN JOIN.

HE HAS TO BECOME A HALF-VAMPIRE TOO!!

WAKU (BOUNCE)

WAKU

PORI (MUNCH) PORI

PICKLED ONIONS

WHAT'S TAKING DARREN SO LONG?

PICK
ONI

CHAPTER 11:
A FALSE CONFESSION

KYU
(TUG)

LET'S TAKE A LITTLE WALK.

WELL...

DID YOU ASK HIM? WHAT DID HE SAY?

TATA
(TEK TEK)

CHAPTER 11:
A FALSE CONFESSION

HE HAS TO BECOME A HALF-VAMPIRE TOO!

WELL, DAR-REN?

WHAT DID MR. CREPSLEY SAY? CAN I JOIN?

DAR-REN...

WHAT DID HE SAY?

I CAN'T PUT HIM THROUGH THE SAME PAIN I'VE HAD TO BEAR...

...BUT I CAN'T TURN HIM INTO A HALF-VAMPIRE.

I WANT TO BE WITH SAM...

GASA

GASA (SHFF)

I HAVE TO MAKE HIM GIVE UP THE IDEA. EVEN IF IT MEANS LYING TO HIM...

I JUST CAN'T!

OH!

GYUUU (CLENCH)

LOOK, WE CAME OUT TO THE ROAD ALREADY!

DON'T DO IT!

WELL, SAM...

WHAT SHOULD WE PLAY?

HEY DARREN, YOU WANT TO COME SEE MY HOUSE? IT'S PRETTY CLOSE BY!

YOU AREN'T ALLOWED TO JOIN THE CIRQUE DU FREAK...

JUST GO HOME, SAM.

IT MEANS I'LL HAVE TO SAY BYE FOR GOOD, WON'T IT...?

DON'T SAY IT...

HUH ...? THE PROBLEM IS ME.

H-HOW COME? DID YOU EXPLAIN THAT I WAS A HARD WORKER!?

I DID.

THEN WHY? WHAT'S THE PROBLEM!?

THEY HAVE TO LOCK ME IN A CAGE.

AT NIGHT, I BECOME LIKE THE WOLF-MAN, SAM...

I GO OUT OF CONTROL. I EAT PEOPLE ...

I WAS ALREADY PUT INTO MY CAGE.

UH...

...YOU DIDN'T SEE ME, REMEMBER?

EXACTLY! AFTER THE CIRCUS...

YOU'RE LYING! AFTER THE CIRCUS...

I MEAN, I KNOW YOU'D NEVER ATTACK ME...

I-I DON'T MIND! I CAN HANDLE IT!

I COULD EASILY CRUSH YOU... JUST LIKE THIS.

GAGO (CRUNCH)

BUT YOU'RE JUST A NORMAL HUMAN BEING, SAM...

EVRA AND MR. CREPSLEY ARE SAFE FROM ME. THEY'RE VERY STRONG.

SOME-TIMES I EVEN GO BERSERK DURING THE DAY...

I WON'T ...

N-NO, DARREN ...

IF YOU STAY WITH ME, THERE'LL BE AN ACCIDENT ...

PARA (CRINK)

PLEASE, SAM. JUST GO.

GET OUT OF HERE!!!

GO, SAM!!

DON'T YOU GET IT?

I DON'T WANT TO EAT MY OWN FRIEND, SAM.

THAT'S THE RIGHT CHOICE, SAM.

THAT'S IT.

THAT'S THE WORLD OF LIGHT, WHERE YOU BELONG.

STAY ON THAT SIDE.

YOU DON'T WANT TO BE ON THIS SIDE...

...OF DEEP, DEEP DARKNESS...

...IN MY LONELY WORLD...

I'VE ALWAYS KNOWN IT.

FURA

FURA (SLUMP)

I KNEW IT WAS TRUE...

WE CAN NEVER CO-EXIST.

HUMANS AND VAMPIRES.

ZUSHA (THWAM)

WHY CAN'T I DREAM OF HAVING A HUMAN FRIEND?

BUT WHAT'S WRONG WITH DREAMING?

JARI (SCRAPE)

FEELING OUT OF IT?

WHAT'S WRONG, DARREN SHAN?

I'M SO SORRY...

I'M SORRY, SAM.

GUGU (HRRG)

120

REALLY
GREAT,
MAN!!!

—BU
(WHOOSH)

I
WAN-
TED TO
THANK
YOU FOR
THE
TICKETS.

I'VE
BEEN
LOOKING
FOR YOU,
MAN.

KARA
(CRACK)

OH, R.V.
IMAGINE
MEETING
YOU HERE.

PASHI

PASHI
(FWAP)

AS
LONG
AS YOU
ENJOYED
YOURSELF.

OH,
THAT'S
NO
PROB-
LEM.

IT WAS
A GREAT
SHOW...

OH
YEAH...

ZUSA
(ZSHH)

W-WHAT'S THE BIG IDEA, R.V.!?

SA
(SWISH)

GAGASA
(GASHHH)

THAT'S WHAT I SHOULD BE ASKIN' YOU!!

LIKE HE WAS SOME KIND OF SAVAGE BEAST!

AND YOU TURNED HIM INTO A SIDESHOW!

HAND-CUFFED AND LOCKED IN A CAGE!

HOW COULD YOU TREAT THAT WOLF-MAN THE WAY YOU DID!?

ARE YOU BEING SERI-OUS?

HUMANS ARE THE WOLF-MAN'S PREY!!

IF THAT'S NATURE'S WAY, THEN TOO BAD!

...HE'D BE KILLING HUMANS LEFT AND RIGHT!

IF WE DIDN'T KEEP HIM IN THAT CAGE...

NO, R.V.! LISTEN!

NO, STOP!

GA (GRAB)

THE FIRST THING I'M DOING IS TURNING YOU IN TO THE POLICE!

YOU PEOPLE ARE THE ANIMALS HERE!

I FIGHT FOR ALL THE POOR, INNOCENT ANIMALS IN THE WORLD!

BUSHU (BSHHT)

H-HE'S STRONG AS HELL... LITTLE BRAT!

SFX: DO (DRIP) DO

GAAAH!!

DOSA (THUMP)

I WASN'T TRYING TO SQUEEZE SO HARD...

S-SORRY, R.V.!

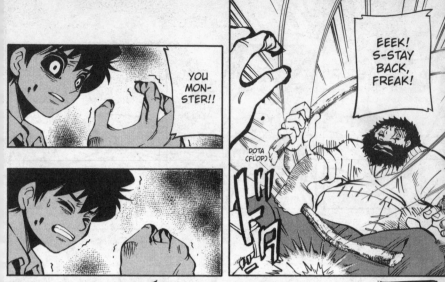

YOU MON-STER!!

EEEK! S-STAY BACK, FREAK!

DOTA
(FLOP)

HOW COULD A HUMAN UNDERSTAND HOW WE FEEL!?

WHAT WOULD YOU KNOW!?

THE WOLF-MAN WOULD BE KILLED IF HE WAS ANY-WHERE BUT AT CIRQUE DU FREAK!!

BUN

A MESSED-UP LITTLE BRAT LIKE YOU...

...IS NOT GOING TO STOP THE BEGINNING OF MY GRAND, HOLY BATTLE!!

SHUT UP! BE QUIET, BE QUIET, BE QUIET!!

BUN (WHOOSH)

ZUZAZA (ZRAHHH)

I'LL RUN IT INTO THE GROUND!

YOUR PRECIOUS CIRCUS IS DONE FOR...

SFX: GIGI (GRRRG)

...:HYPOCRITE!!!

YOU...

BA (ZWIP)

GUA
(GRAHHH)

AAAHHH!!!

AAAAA!!!

W- WHAT'S GOING OOOON!?

HUH...!!?

126

YOU'RE A MONSTER...

W-WHAT ARE YOU...?

SFX: GATA (SHIVER) GATA

YOU SHOULD SEE WHAT SOME OF THE OTHERS ARE LIKE!

GI (GLARE)

YEAH. BUT I'M ONLY A BABY MONSTER.

BASHAAN (SPLAASH)

H-HELP, POLICE!! EEEEEK!!

MONSTER!!!

BASHA

BASHA (SPLASH)

IT'S A MONSTER!

EEEEK!

AAAHH!

GAYA
CIRQUE D'FREAK

GAYA
(HUSTLE)

...BEFORE THE POLICE HAVE TIME TO COME HERE...

I SUPPOSE WE SHALL PULL UP OUR ROOTS AND MOVE WHEN TONIGHT'S PERFORMANCE IS OVER...

I'M HESITANT TO CANCEL ON SUCH SHORT NOTICE.

UNFORTU- NATELY, WE ALREADY HAVE A SHOW SCHEDULED FOR TONIGHT.

IT WAS GOOD OF YOU TO INFORM ME.

YES, SIR...

YES, MR. TALL!

NOW, DARREN, WILL YOU INFORM THE OTHER MEMBERS OF THIS PLAN?

THIS ISN'T THE FIRST TIME WE'VE CLASHED WITH THE AUTHORI- TIES.

DON'T BE TROU- BLED.

WE HAVE BEEN HERE LONG ENOUGH...

I DIDN'T MEAN FOR THIS TO HAPPEN...

I'M SORRY.

ZAWA (MURMUR)

ZAWA

CHAPTER 12:
THE LAST NIGHT

AND THAT'S THE END OF THE PACKING...

...Y-YEAH...

MAYBE THAT'S ALL FOR THE BETTER, THOUGH...

IT DOESN'T SEEM LIKE WE'LL GET THE CHANCE TO SAY GOOD-BYE TO SAM.

JUST THE STARS...

THEY'RE SO BEAUTIFUL...

HUH? ME?

WHAT-CHA LOOKIN' AT?

CHAPTER 12:
THE LAST NIGHT

URGH...

I DIDN'T KNOW YOU LIKED STARS SO MUCH, EVRA.

SO DO I...

YOU CAN'T SEE STARS AS WELL IN THE CITY.

I'LL MISS THIS PLACE WHEN WE GO.

SORRY...

LET'S TAKE A BREAK.

NOT FEELING TOO GOOD?

I'LL BE FINE. I'VE BEEN BETTER, THOUGH.

STILL NOT DRINKING HUMAN BLOOD?

...I'LL BE EVIL.

I'M AFRAID THAT IF I DRINK HUMAN BLOOD...

YEAH, MAYBE...

...BUT CAN'T YOU JUST THINK OF THE BLOOD AS MEDICINE OR SOMETHING?

LOOK, I DON'T KNOW MUCH ABOUT WHAT YOU'RE GOING THROUGH...

ANY-ONE WHO LOOKS AT HUMANS AS IF THEY'RE ANIMALS MUST BE EVIL!

MR. CREPSLEY SAYS VAMPIRES AREN'T EVIL, BUT I THINK THEY ARE.

YOU KNOW, SOMETHING YOU HAVE TO DRINK TO SURVIVE...

WHAT IF I KILL SOME- ONE?

AND WHAT IF I CAN'T CONTROL MY THIRST?

YOU'RE NOT EVIL, DAR- REN!

I DON'T THINK YOU COULD!

I'D MISS YOU...

DAR- REN ...

WOULD YOU ACTU- ALLY DO THAT?

...WOULD YOU REALLY LET YOURSELF DIE RATHER THAN DRINK?

EVRA ...

...IF YOU DIED...

OKAY...

THANKS.

SHOW'S GONNA START ANY MINUTE NOW.

SUTA (HOP)

WELL, I SHOULD BE GOING.

I'LL WAKE YOU UP WHEN THE SHOW'S OVER...

YOU SHOULD LIE DOWN AND GET SOME REST.

I'VE PROBABLY GOT TWO OR THREE DAYS LEFT, AT MOST...

FURA

FURA (WOBBLE)

...WHEN YOUR TIME TO DIE COMES.

IT'S WEIRD... MAYBE IT IS EASY TO TELL...

JARA (CLANK)

IT'S NOT FAIR...

THEY DON'T HAVE TO STRESS ABOUT DRINKING HUMAN BLOOD OR DYING.

...THEIR ONLY TROUBLES ARE SCHOOL AND FRIENDS.

FOR MOST KIDS MY AGE...

JARA

I WONDER WHAT IT'S LIKE TO DIE FOR REAL.

YORO (LURCH)

THE SOUND OF CHAINS?

I HAVE A BAD FEELING...

THERE IT IS AGAIN!

WHICH WAY IS IT COMING FROM?

ZAWA (RUSTLE)

ZAWA

ZAWA

WHAT'S THAT SOUND?

SFX: JARA (CLANK)

BAKIIN (CRAKK)

IT COULD BE—!

DA (DASH)

ZA (ZSHH)

R.V.
!!?

I'M JUST FOLLOWING MY BELIEFS! THIS IS MY BATTLE!!

I'M FREEING THIS POOR, ABUSED CREATURE!

STAY OUT OF THIS!

WHAT ARE YOU DOING? STOP!

BA (CLEAP)

AAH!

ZUZA (ZSHH)

IS THAT WHAT YOU THINK?

STOP, R.V.! GET AWAY FROM THE CAGE! HE'LL KILL YOU!

I'VE ALREADY CALLED THE POLICE! YOU PEOPLE ARE FINISHED!

...THEY WILL ALWAYS BEHAVE IN KIND!

IF, ON THE OTHER HAND, YOU TREAT THEM WITH RESPECT, LOVE, AND HUMANITY...

IF YOU TREAT THEM LIKE CRAZY MONSTERS, THEY'LL ACT THAT WAY.

IT'S BEEN MY EXPERIENCE THAT ANIMALS REACT ACCORDING TO HOW THEY'RE TREATED.

GIGI (GRRG)

YOU WON'T PREVENT ME FROM DOING MY DUTY!!

NO! YOU WON'T STOP ME!

THE WOLF-MAN ISN'T LIKE OTHER ANIMALS! GET AWAY FROM HIM!

STOP, R.V.!!

I'M GOING TO FREE EVERY CHAINED ANIMAL IN THE WORLD!!

THESE...

BUSHU (SPLURT)

... HANDS? HANDS!?

MUSHA (CHOMP)

BARI (CHOMP)

MUSHA (MUNCH)

... AND ...

BAKI (CRUNCH)

I'LL CUT HIS CHAINS WITH THESE HANDS, AND...

BOGU (CRSHH)

#BAG! (CRACK)

MY HANDS EXIST TO DO THE WORK OF GOOD!!

MUSHA
(MUNCH)

MUSHA

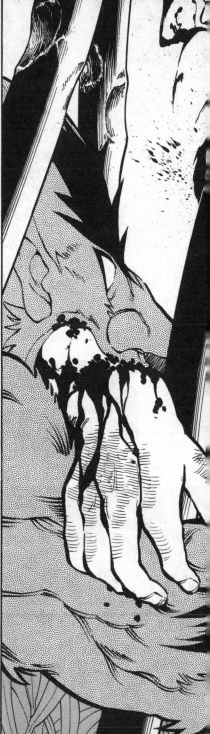

MUSHI
(GRRK)

SA
(LUNGE)

GIVE THEM BACK, WOLF-MAN!!

MUSHA
(MULSH)

URP!

BOGI
(CRONK)

YOU HORRIBLE BEAST! HOW DARE YOU...

YOU'RE AN EVIL LITTLE MONSTER, AND YOU STOLE MY HANDS!

WE HAVE TO TAKE CARE OF YOUR ARMS BEFORE YOU BLEED TO DEATH!

THIS IS YOUR FAULT! YOU TOOK MY HANDS!

AAAH! MY HANDS! WHERE ARE MY HANDS!?

HANDS!

HANDS!

HANDS!

HI

HI

HI (CHEE)

HI

HI

HI

HI

MY HANDS! MY HANDS! MY HANDS!

HEE HEE HEE! HEE HEE HEE HEE!

JARA
(CLINK)

UM...
R.V.?

GII
(CREAK)

BAKI
(CRAK)

: : : : : : : :
!!

OH
NO!!

GASA
(SKSHH)

I'M
SAVED
...

GACHI
(SHIVER)
GACHI

I'M...

NO, THE
BLOOD
LEADS IN
THE OTHER
DIRECTION.

WAS HE
CHASING
R.V.?

BUT WHY
DIDN'T HE
ATTACK
ME?

THEN...
WHO?

NO...IT CAN'T BE...

GASA
(RUMMAGE)
GASA

PORO
(PLOP)

THIS BAG...

KORON
(THUNK)

SAM'S IN DANGER!!

Sam Grest

HOW COULD YOU BE SO STUPID, SAM!?

THE WOLF-MAN'S AFTER SAM!

WHERE IS HE? WHICH WAY!?

GOT TO FOLLOW THE WOLF-MAN'S STENCH!

SAM!!!

GI
(CREAK)

I CAN'T BEAT THE WOLF-MAN WITH THIS METAL ROD...

DOKI
(BA-THUMP)

GISHI

GISHI
(CREAK)

GA
(GRAB)

BU
(WHOOSH)

YAAAH!!!

I'LL FIGHT HIM OFF! HE'LL SEE!!

WELL, I'M NOT GONNA LET HIM EAT ME!

SAM!

DARREN!!!

I JUST HAD TO SNEAK IN...

I'M SORRY...

THANK GOD YOU'RE SAFE, SAM!

GOTO (THUD)

DARREN!

UOOOOOOOON (AWOOOOOOO)

GYORO

GYORO (SPIN)

I WON'T LET HIM TAKE SAM FROM ME...

RIGHT NOW WE'VE GOT TO GET OUT OF HERE ALIVE!

WE'LL TALK LATER, SAM.

I'LL KEEP HIM ALIVE!!!

WHAT IS IT, MR. CREPS-LEY?

EVRA.

NO ...

HE ISN'T SLEEP-ING IN HIS TENT?

HAVE YOU SEEN DAR-REN?

I TOLD HIM TO GO LIE DOWN JUST MINUTES AGO.

THAT'S ODD...

CHAPTER 13:
BLOOD AND SPIRIT

IF WE HOLE OURSELVES UP IN THAT WAREHOUSE WITH THE TOUGH-LOOKING IRON DOOR, EVEN THE WOLF-MAN WON'T BE ABLE TO GET US.

OVER THERE, DARREN.

LET'S SPRINT FOR IT TOGETHER, BEFORE HE NOTICES US!!

OKAY. WE'LL HIDE IN THERE AND WAIT FOR HELP FROM THE CIRQUE...

AAAH!!

GAKU
(HURK)

DA
(DASH)

R
U
N
!!

WE CAN'T BOTH MAKE IT FROM THIS DISTANCE!

GURURURU (GRRRRR)

ZUSHA— (ZSHH)

HUH? NO, DARREN! COME ON!

RUN, SAM!

DON'T WORRY! THAT WOLF-MAN WON'T GET PAST ME.

HUMANS AND VAMPIRES WILL NEVER CO-EXIST!

I'LL STOP HIM RIGHT HERE.

...AND DIE A HUMAN !!!

I'LL SAVE SAM...

GIRO (GLARE)

BAKI

DO (WHACK)

I CAN'T ABANDON A FRIEND!

WE HAVE TO GO TO-GETH-ER!

SAM!? WHY DIDN'T YOU RUN!?

NOW,
SAM!
GET
AWAY!

SAM
...

...

SAM
...

BAGI
(GRUNCH)

GUSHU
(SPLURCH)

BARI
(RIP)

GAGO
(CRUNCH)

GARU
(GRR)

BASA
(FLAP)

GASHI
(SNATCH)

GYU
(ZWOOM)

MISHI
(CRIK)

ZUGA
(CRUNCH)

BELIEVE IT OR NOT...

...I CAME AS SOON AS I COULD, DARREN...

HAA

HAA
(HUFF)

S-SAM...

...

SAM!!!

DO
(SHOVE)

SAM!!

S-SAM...

JIWA
(BLOOM)

OH, SAM!
NO...

THIS CAN'T BE HAPPENING!

PASA
(FLAP)

JUST...
WANTED...
TO BE...
WITH YOU...

I'M...
SORRY
...

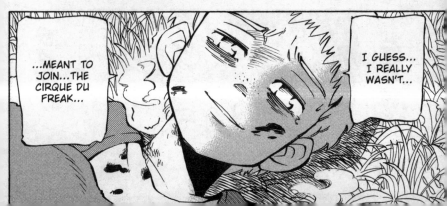

...MEANT TO JOIN...THE CIRQUE DU FREAK...

I GUESS...
I REALLY
WASN'T...

I AM AFRAID IT IS TOO LATE FOR THAT, DARREN. MOST OF HIS INSIDES HAVE BEEN DEVOURED...

NO DOUBT HE CANNOT EVEN FEEL THE PAIN ANY-MORE...

SAM!!

GEHO (COUGH)

GEHO

HELP! HELP HIM!

SEAL UP HIS WOUNDS, NOW!

YOU CAN STILL BE ANYTHING YOU WANT! AS LONG AS YOU GROW UP ...!!

DYING WON'T DO ANYTHING FOR YOU!

NO, SAM! YOU CAN'T DIE!!

HUH ...?

BUT THERE IS SOME-THING WE CAN DO FOR HIS SPIRIT.

HE WILL BE DEAD IN MOMENTS. IT IS UN-AVOIDABLE.

SNIFF...

SNIFF...

CHAPTER 13:
TOGETHER WITH SAM

I...

...

YOU MUST DRINK SAM'S BLOOD...

...DARREN.

HOW DARE YOU SUGGEST THAT!

I WON'T DO ANYTHING OF THE SORT!!

SAM'S DYING, BUT ALL YOU'RE WORRIED ABOUT IS BLOODING ME!

SHUT UP!!

ABOUT HOW VAMPIRES CAN ABSORB PART OF A PERSON'S SOUL BY DRINKING THEIR BLOOD?

DO YOU REMEMBER OUR DISCUSSION?

BUT IF YOU DRINK FROM SAM AND ABSORB PART OF HIS ESSENCE, YOU WILL NOT LOSE ALL OF HIM.

LOSING A LOVED ONE IS HARD.

ONCE THEY ARE DEAD, THEY ARE GONE FOREVER.

DO YOU REMEMBER?

DARREN, THIS IS IMPORTANT.

KOKU (NOD)

I... CAN'T DO IT...

I CAN'T...

HIS SPIRIT WILL LIVE ON INSIDE YOU...

YOU WANT ME... TO KILL SAM?

!!!

DRINK... DARREN...

I'M NOT A NORMAL HUMAN...

SAM, I'M SORRY...

THEN I CAN BE TOGETH-ER...WITH YOU AND EVRA... FOREVER...

...I WANT YOU TO DRINK...

IF I CAN LIVE ON INSIDE YOU...

I MEAN...

I'M NOT... SCARED...

I DON'T CARE IF YOU'RE A VAM-PIRE...

...WE'RE FRIENDS... AREN'T WE?

... SAM ...

GYUUU...
(SQUEEEZE)

I'M SORRY ...

PA
(PSHHH)

PI
(FLICK)

GOKU
(GULP)

MORNING!

TICKET: CIRQUE DU FREAK

IF ONLY YOU'D NEVER MET ME!

GOKU

GOKU (GULP)

I'M SORRY... SO SORRY, SAM.

176

WAS THAT A LIE...?

WHEN YOU SAID... YOU ATE PEOPLE...

DAR... REN...

...TO PRO-TECT ME...

THANKS FOR LYING...

GOKU

I... HAD... FUN...

GOKU

...AHH...

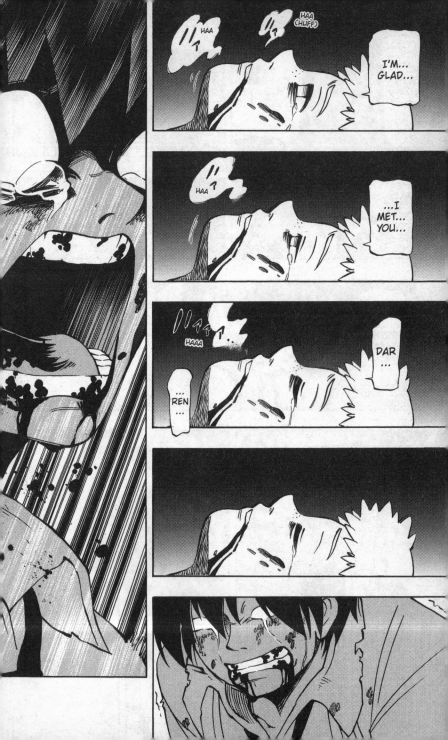

BUROROMU
(VRUMM)

I DO NOT KNOW IF DARREN WOULD AGREE...

THANK HEAVEN FOR SMALL MERCIES.

NO, I MERELY KNOCKED HIM OUT.

IS THE WOLF-MAN DEAD?

カ" (ROLLS)
ガラ GARA

カ"
ガラ GARA

EVRA...

DARREN.

WHERE DID THEY PUT SAM?

THEY'LL FIND HIM SOON, AND HIS PARENTS CAN GIVE HIM A CEREMONY.

WE'VE TIPPED OFF THE POLICE...

HE'S GONE NOW. FIRMLY BURIED...

...HELPED ME BURY SAM.

THAT LITTLE PERSON WITH THE LIMP...

ZUZU (DRAG)

HYOI (HOP)

DOSUN (PLOP)

...BUT HE'S A BIT DIFFERENT FROM THE REST.

I CAN'T TELL THE OTHERS APART...

JI
(STARE)

I DON'T KNOW, AND I DON'T WANT TO KNOW...

WHERE'S R.V.?

LOOK, DARREN... I'M GLAD AT LEAST YOU SUR- VIVED...

...

THERE'S A PART OF HIM INSIDE YOU, ISN'T THERE?

LET'S TRAVEL THE WORLD AND EXPERIENCE TONS OF THINGS.

WE'LL HELP SAM SEE AND DO THE THINGS HE NEVER GOT TO DO.

YOU DRANK THAT BLOOD FOR SAM'S SAKE.

YOU DID A GOOD THING.

182

THOUGHT YOU MIGHT WANT IT.

SU (SHH)

I...I FOUND THIS.

...DOESN'T SEEM REAL, THOUGH.

IT STILL...

Sam Gre

HEY...

LOOK, DAR-REN.

SFX: MUNYU (MMPH) MUNYU

AND SO WE LEFT OUR CAMP-GROUND AND STARTED OFF ON A LONG, LONG JOURNEY.

AND IN MY HEART, SAM GREST TRAVELLED WITH US AS WE HEADED INTO THE LIGHT...

THE VAMPIRE'S ASSISTANT - END

A QUICK GUIDE TO THE STORY OF THE *CIRQUE DU FREAK* MANGA VERSION (SORT OF)!! PART 2!!

AFTER-WORD SPECIAL

UOOOO (RAHHHH)

OOO (AHHH)

VOLUME 2 WAS A POINT WHERE I TRULY LEARNED THE DIFFERENCE IN DEPICTION BETWEEN A NOVEL AND A MANGA.

PORI (MUNCH) PORI

OH, SAM...

DEPICTION IS A VERY FUN YET EXASPERATING PROCESS.

PART 1

NOVEL VS. MANGA

I SEE!

THIS WAS NEW TO ME, SINCE I HAD ONLY DRAWN SELF-CONTAINED SHORT STORIES BEFORE THIS.

A WEEKLY SERIAL ALSO MEANS YOU HAVE TO CRAM A HOOK AND CLIMAX INTO AN EIGHTEEN-PAGE CHAPTER EVERY SINGLE WEEK.

BECAUSE A MANGA HAS ART, IT HAS A TENDENCY TO COME ACROSS MUCH MORE STRAIGHTFORWARD THAN A NOVEL.

"GUTS"!?

"BLOODY MESS"!?

GABIIIN (BONGGG)

"HIS ARMS WERE BITTEN OFF"!?

CIRQUE DU FREAK 2 TAUGHT ME THAT A SERIAL IS JUST A SERIES OF EIGHTEEN-PAGE SHORT STORIES.

SCENES HAD TO BE HEARTLESSLY REMOVED TO MAKE THE STORY FIT...

PART 2

CHARACTERS AND IMAGE

I FIND THE LETTERS FROM FANS OF THE ORIGINAL NOVELS ESPECIALLY INTERESTING, AS THEY OFTEN COME WITH THE READER'S OWN SKETCH OF THE CHARACTERS AS THEY SEE THEM.

NEAT!

OOOOH!

DO (BLUSH) "..."

I LOVE GETTING SUPPORTIVE LETTERS FROM READERS EVERY SINGLE WEEK.

IT'S QUITE FASCINATING SEEING SO MANY DIFFERENT DESIGNS.

LIKE A COOL, BLOND DARREN, A BLACK-HAIRED STEVE...

KILL WITH YOUR GAZE!

...A CUTE CREPSLEY, AND VERY HANDSOME MR. TALL.

WHEE!

THAT'S THE GREAT PART ABOUT NOVELS!

IT REALLY BRINGS HOME THE FACT THAT A HUNDRED DIFFERENT READERS WILL HAVE A HUNDRED DIFFERENT MENTAL IMAGES OF DARREN.

WHAT IS DARREN'S NEXT ADVENTURE, AFTER HIS TRAGIC FAREWELL TO SAM? LET US MEET AGAIN IN THE MANGA TUNNELS OF BLOOD!

BREAKING NEWS! IS THIS THE IDEAL PORTRAIT OF DARREN!?

HA HA HA!

?

SNIFF! BLISS!

OF COURSE, THERE ARE ALSO MANY PEOPLE WHO DO ILLUSTRATIONS OF THE MANGA VERSION. THIS MAKES ME SO HAPPY, I CRY! THANK YOU ALL!

CHAN COUND CHAN

I BET IT WOULD BE COOL TO BLEND EVERYONE'S IMAGINARY DARREN INTO ONE USING A COMPUTER!

THE SAGA OF DARREN SHAN ②
The Vampire's Assistant

Darren Shan
Takahiro Arai

Translation: Stephen Paul
Lettering: AndWorld Design
Original cover design: Hitoshi SHIRAYAMA + Bay Bridge Studio

Darren Shan Vol. 2
Text © 2007 Darren Shan, Artworks © 2007 Takahiro ARAI
All rights reserved
Original Japanese edition published in Japan in 2007
by Shogakukan Inc., Tokyo
Artwork reproduction rights in U.K. and The Commonwealth arranged
with Shogakukan Inc. through Tuttle-Mori Agency, Inc., Tokyo.

English translations © Darren Shan 2009

Published in Great Britain by Harper Collins *Children's Books* 2009
Harper Collins *Children's Books* is a division of HarperCollins *Publishers* Ltd
77-85 Fulham Palace Road, Hammersmith, London, W6 8JB

www.harpercollins.co.uk

ISBN: 978 0 00 732088 2

Printed and bound in Great Britain by Clays Ltd, St Ives plc

Mixed Sources
Product group from well-managed
forests and other controlled sources
www.fsc.org Cert no. SW-COC-1806
© 1996 Forest Stewardship Council
FSC

FSC is a non-profit international organisation established to promote the
responsible management of the world's forests. Products carrying the FSC
label are independently certified to assure consumers that they come
from forests that are managed to meet the social, economic and
ecological needs of present and future generations.

Find out more about HarperCollins and the environment at
www.harpercollins.co.uk/green